# On Tour with
# THOMAS TELFORD

CHRIS MORRIS took up photography after dropping out of university. The late Sixties saw him working for Italian magazines who were avid for images of the London arts and hippy scene.

After three decades of corporate photography he moved to Gloucestershire and reverted to documentary work, linking it to his long interest in industrial history. He has held several exhibitions of his work and published a number of books, including:

*Work in the Woods*
A celebration of the Forest of Dean's industrial legacy

*Under Blorenge Mountain*
Exploring the Blaenavon World Heritage Site

*The Great Brunel*
Photographing the legacy of the great Victorian engineer

*A Portrait of the Severn*
Evocative images of Britain's longest and most important river

# *On Tour with*
# THOMAS TELFORD

## Chris Morris

*Introduction by*

### Neil Cossons, Chairman of English Heritage

TANNER'S YARD PRESS

*To my daughter Rachel, who travelled with me on my first iron bridge tour in 1980*

First published 2004 by Tanners Yard Press
Second edition 2006

Tanners Yard Press  Church Road  Longhope  GL17 0LA
*www.tannersyardpress.co.uk*

Designed by Paul Manning
Printed and bound by Gutenberg Press Limited, Malta

British Library Cataloguing in Publication Data
A catalogue record for this book is available from the British Library

ISBN 0-9542096-6-4 (2006)
ISBN 978-0-9542096-6-7 (2007)

*Page 1:* Bust of Thomas Telford at the Institution of Civil Engineers
*Page 6:* The Menai Bridge with Snowdonia in the background
*Page 8:* The Caledonian Canal at Moy

*Note:* For reasons of historical context, some Welsh placenames in the book appear in their anglicised version.

# CONTENTS

'It is more by the performance of useful works than the enjoyment of splendid orders I wish my name to be known'

*Thomas Telford, on hearing he had been knighted by the King of Sweden*

# PREFACE TO THE SECOND EDITION

This book is a visual celebration of Thomas Telford's engineering and architecture, much of which remains today. It is not intended to be a complete catalogue; while all the major works are included, many minor ones are not (particularly in Scotland, where there are literally hundreds of road bridges and dozens of churches to be found). There is little mention of work which no longer exists.

The book's title, *On Tour with Thomas Telford*, is a reflection of the great man's itinerant lifestyle and suggests a geographical format. But it also flows roughly chronologically – many of the projects took several years to realise and so ran concurrently. The book is not academic or technical, but each chapter provides enough information to view the images in context.

If Telford could come on tour today he would find many changes to his works – bridges widened and strengthened, harbours extended, churches embellished; he would also find canals meticulously maintained (though nowadays for recreation rather than commerce). He would come upon other bridges that, by-passed, stand as monuments to his genius, and if he visited his churches at Mallinslea and Madeley he would find himself in the centre of a modern metropolis named after him.

I have not disguised these changes for I believe that despite them Telford's original concepts shine through. Neither have I tried to isolate his works in a time warp: in fact, I have embraced facets of modern life that happily interact with his two-hundred-year-old legacy.

For this second edition I have added new material from the Welsh Borders, the Pennines and Scotland's far north, as well as allowing more space for the important Birmingham Canal improvements. The year 2007 is the 250th anniversary of Telford's birth. Nothing could be more appropriate for a man whose life was dedicated to his work than to view his achievements as a kind of visual biography. I hope that through this book many more people will appreciate this great man and perhaps salute him with tours of their own.

*Chris Morris*
*October 2006*

# INTRODUCTION *by Neil Cossons, Chairman of English Heritage*

Thomas Telford was one of the giants of his age, a man of boundless energy and intellectual curiosity who helped to define the nineteenth century as the heroic age of engineering. The first President of the Institution of Civil Engineers, Telford more than any other established engineering as a profession. And two hundred years later, today's engineers would find his practices familiar; his ability to design, specify and delegate and to put together a team of trained and trusted surveyors, foremen and masons. In this way his prolific output could be translated into the abundance of great works that span the country and by which we now recognise and revere him.

In this book Chris Morris brings to life through his vivid portfolio of photographs the bold inventiveness of a man whose genius can be appreciated as much for its elegance and artistry as its engineering vigour. At the time of their building Telford's works commanded awe and esteem. They conferred certainty on the emerging world of industrial and mercantile prosperity by forging the essential links on which trade and commerce could depend. And they fuelled the debate on the sublime and the picturesque which absorbed the attentions of contemporary writers and artists. Of the entrance to the Caledonian Canal, which he visited with Telford in 1819, Southey wrote, 'here we see the powers of nature brought to act upon a great scale, in subservience to the purposes of men'. Telford's roads, bridges, canals and harbours demonstrate clearly and powerfully the triumph of mankind over nature in the interests of creating a universal good.

It is this absence of ambiguity that sets Telford's works apart. That spirit of unbridled self-confidence is as compelling today as when they were built, a generation or more before the horrors of industrialisation that have clouded our view of the middle years of the nineteenth century. A passage through the Caledonian or Gotha canals or along the Wales section of the Holyhead Road exhilarates as no other. But if at the time Telford was affirming a mastery over the physical world, today his works, softened by time and nature, enjoy an extraordinary affinity with the landscapes of which they form part. Almost without exception his engineering design complements rather than despoils. If there are exceptions, they were never built. His proposal for spanning the Avon Gorge in Bristol – with 'Gothic' towers rising from the water's edge – is difficult to take seriously, whereas what is arguably his masterpiece, the crossing of the straits of Menai, must stand as one of the great works of art and engineering of all time.

Throughout, Chris Morris draws on detail to emphasise this apparent sensitivity to setting and place. Telford was an enthusiastic proponent of cast-iron for bridge construction, perfecting at Bonar, at the head of Dornoch Firth, a design he was to use again at Craigellachie, and later at Esk Bridge, Carlisle and Mythe Bridge, Tewkesbury. But it was at Bettws-y-Coed that he adapted this pattern for the dramatic setting of the Conwy valley to shrewdly celebrate in slogan and symbols Wellington's victory at Waterloo, on a road paid for by government funds in order to ease the journey for Irish parliamentarians travelling from Dublin to Westminster. The giant cast-iron roses, thistles, leeks and shamrocks that fill the spandrel frames represent a rare departure into decoration.

There was more to Telford than meets the eye. But what Chris Morris has so beautifully captured here meets the eye in a most seemly manner. It is a prelude to the tour that must follow.

# 1 EARLY WORK: MASON AND ARCHITECT

Thomas Telford was born in 1757, in an isolated cottage north of Langholm in the Scottish borders; within months his father, a shepherd, had died. It is difficult to imagine a tougher start in life. With the help of an uncle Telford attended parish school; the benefit of an education was at least matched by the lasting friendships he made which served him well throughout his life.

Telford was apprenticed to a stone mason in Langholm and developed an ambition to be an architect. He furthered his prospects with a spell in Edinburgh's burgeoning 'New Town', then in London where he was a mason on Somerset House. His progress was linked to the rocketing social status of a childhood friend who married an heiress from Bath, adopted his new wife's name, Pulteney, and became one of the wealthiest men in the country.

His friendship with William Pulteney secured Telford a foreman's job on works at Portsmouth dockyard and in 1787 precipitated a move to Shrewsbury.

## Shrewsbury

As part of his estate, William Pulteney had inherited the rather ruinous castle, and rebuilding it was Telford's first task. Another early project in the town was to improve the county gaol: Telford revised the plans after meeting the prison reformer John Howard, whose humanity made a deep impression on him.

## Churches and bridges

Nothing had so far disturbed Telford's architectural ambitions, exemplified by churches he was responsible for at Madeley and Mallinslea (in the modern town of Telford) and at Bridgnorth. However, by 1788 he had been appointed County Surveyor with the responsibility for Shropshire's roads and bridges.

His first bridge (since his journeyman work at Langholm) was at Montford, over the Severn. Following the floods of 1793 he replaced those at Bewdley and Bridgnorth, sturdily workmanlike in stone and still in use today. But more significant was the new bridge at Buildwas, sadly replaced. Just down the river from Shrewsbury, an inescapably short distance away at Coalbrookdale, stood famously, then as now, the Iron Bridge. Telford would have seized on this example of what could be achieved with the new material, cast iron, and looked to exploit its potential. Buildwas gave him a chance; arguing for a single span for ease of navigation and flood resistance, he made it both longer and lighter than the pioneering arch at Coalbrookdale.

## Canals

Telford's bridge-building might lead us into thinking he was changing his career, but it was a further development which was to become the turning point. In 1793, while still at Shrewsbury, he was appointed 'general agent, engineer and architect' to the newly formed Ellesmere Canal Company.

*Facing page: Somerset House*

*Telford's birthplace near Langholm in the Scottish borders was a bleak area of tumbling streams and high sheep pasture. His early work included the gravestone (left) for his father in the burial ground at Westerkirk.*

*In the town itself is a stone doorway by Telford (above), probably made as a training exercise.*

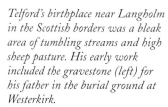

*Before he headed south to seek his fortune, Telford worked as a mason in Edinburgh New Town (above).*

*Facing page: Boys throw stones into the Esk at Langholm Bridge, where Telford worked as an apprentice mason.*

*Left: The south-west corner of Somerset House in London, where Telford worked as a mason.*

*In Portsmouth Naval Dockyard, Telford was employed as superintendent for new buildings, including the chapel, St John's Church (facing page).*

*Right: The brief for the Commissioner's House – today the home of the Second Sea Lord – included its 'suitability for the reception of Royal visitors'; the red carpet may be a later touch.*

While at Shrewsbury, Telford rebuilt the gaol (facing page) and the castle (left), where today Peter Downward is a warder for the Shropshire Regimental Museum.

Below: Under the influence of the penal reformer John Howard, who felt prisoners should be given meaningful employment (and whose bust sits in the niche above the gaol entrance), Telford used convict labour to help with archaeological excavations at the nearby Roman site of Uriconium (Wroxeter).

In 1792 Telford built Montford Bridge (facing page), his first since apprentice work in Langholm. The date stone reads 1792. Further upriver, on Pultney's estates at Haimwood (right), he supervised works to control flooding of the low-lying meadows – a series of 'levées' (known locally as 'argys') and a drain still called New Cut.

Telford's first bridge over the
Severn at Montford (see page 19)
was built in 1792. Those at
Bewdley (facing page) and
Bridgnorth (right) followed three
years later.

Also at Bridgnorth, St Mary
Magdalene (above) was Telford's
first church in Shropshire.

*St Leonard's, Mallinslea (above), and St Michael's, Madeley (above right, right and facing page). The mosaic floor may be a later addition.*

*Right: five iron caps define the position of the ribs of Telford's first iron bridge at Buildwas; above them, the modern crossing rises from the old stone abutments. A remnant of one of the outer ribs with the date cast in it survives as a memorial (far right).*

*Below right: an 1818 bridge from Cound, removed and renovated, carries a footpath in Telford town centre.*

*Facing page: Aston Cantlop, 1813, is the only Telford-designed Shropshire iron bridge remaining in situ.*

*Buildwas was cast at Coalbrook-dale, while the later ones were in partnership with William Hazeldine (see page 27).*

# 2 ELLESMERE CANAL: A CAREER SHIFT

**Shrewsbury canal**

While the planning of the Ellesmere canal was still in its early stages, Telford's services were sought by the directors of the half-built Shrewsbury canal. One of the works on this route was an aqueduct over the River Tern at Longdon, of which all that existed was a conventional brick-built approach to the river. What Telford added to this was nothing short of revolutionary.

The accepted way of building aqueducts, inherited from the original canal master-builder James Brindley and practised unamended by his successors, Jessop and Rennie, was to make massive structures substantial enough to be lined with a thick layer of puddled clay. Inevitably they were squat and bulbous. Telford was prepared to experiment with iron, creating a trough made of flanged and bolted plates, supported by an iron frame.

**Ellesmere canal**

The Ellesmere canal company had an ambitious plan to link the Mersey and the Dee with the Severn. By the time Telford was appointed in 1793, much debate about routes had already taken place. Telford's position was secondary to the chief engineer, William Jessop, an older man with long experience and a high reputation as a canal builder; nevertheless, it was Telford's task to plan and build the canal, with Jessop taking a monitoring role. While the novice must have learned a lot from the master, credit for the great works that followed belongs to the younger man.

The Ellesmere never met its aims. Its plan to push north up the west side of the Dee (to serve the rich industrial area of Ruabon and Wrexham) was abandoned in favour of a tramway, and its southern line, heading for the Severn, ended ignominiously at a wharf near the village of Weston

*Facing page: Pontcysyllte*

Lullingfields. The northern link from Chester to the Mersey was built, as were the planned branches to Llanymynech (connecting with the Montgomeryshire canal at Carreghofa) and through Ellesmere to Whitchurch. The Whitchurch line was extended to reach the Chester canal just north of Nantwich, and thus a rather diversionary but through route was created from Llangollen to the Mersey. But before the original plans were aborted Telford had conceived and built a wonder of the age – the Pontcysyllte Aqueduct – by which the canal crossed the Vale of Llangollen.

It is tempting to see Longdon as a model for this great aqueduct, but in fact Pontcysyllte's drawings pre-date Longdon (though its building could be seen as a testbed for Telford's ideas). Pontcysyllte, 120 feet above the River Dee, was too high for an iron frame, but it did again utilise an iron trough; this time arches made of flanged and bolted iron ran beneath, supported in turn on slim, tapering stone columns made possible by the relative lightness of the canal above.

Just to the south were two more innovative structures. From a distance, the Chirk aqueduct appears to be a conventional masonry viaduct, of inadequate size to carry a canal; this relative lightness of appearance is due to the use of flanged and bolted iron plates as a lining rather than puddled clay. Immediately at the aqueduct's north end the canal dives into a tunnel provided with a towpath – an unusual feature for the time.

In admiring Telford's new structures it would be wrong to ignore the part played by his collaborator William Hazeldine, who supplied all the cast iron for these works. Hazeldine's foundry was Plas Kynaston, directly linked to the canal at the north end of Pontcysyllte.

*William Clowes had started to build an aqueduct to carry the Shrewsbury canal over the river Tern, using a conventional squat and heavy design to take the weight of the puddled clay which would line the canal bed (above).*

*Telford took a radically different approach: his use of flanged and bolted iron plates was an unprecedented and revelatory use of the new material. The towpath (above right) is slung alongside the main structure.*

*The aqueduct, standing unannounced in farmland (facing page), is a classic monument to industrial progress.*

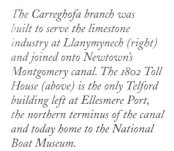

*The Ellesmere canal failed in its objective to reach Shrewsbury and the Severn (see page 27), terminating near the village of Weston Lullingfields. Today the hamlet of Weston Wharf still boasts a wide green ditch, and a building that appears to owe more to commerce than agriculture (left). This probable warehouse may have seen the transit of the wrought-iron chains from Hazeldine's forge near Shrewsbury en route to the Menai Bridge (see page 84).*

*The Carreghofa branch was built to serve the limestone industry at Llanymynech (right) and joined onto Newtown's Montgomery canal. The 1802 Toll House (above) is the only Telford building left at Ellesmere Port, the northern terminus of the canal and today home to the National Boat Museum.*

*Facing page: Horseshoe Falls, west of Llangollen on the river Dee, provides the water supply for the Ellesmere canal.*

## TREVOR BASIN

*To the east of Llangollen and immediately north of Pontcysyllte, Trevor was an important wharf in Telford's day (and still is, for holiday traffic).*

*The archway (top right) may have taken a canal extension to Plas Kynaston, William Hazeldine's iron foundry – a perfect location for building the aqueduct.*

*The route north to Ruabon, originally planned to be served by the Ellesmere canal, was connected by a tramway (bottom right).*

*The house Telford is reputed to have stayed in when visiting Plas Kynaston and Pontcysyllte is now a public house named 'The Telford'. The fanlight (above right) celebrates the connection.*

*Just below Trevor, a Telford tourist can enjoy breakfast with a grandstand view of the aqueduct at Elaine's B & B (right).*

*Facing page: There are several iron and stone hybrid bridges at Trevor Basin; instead of being built on timber centering, which was removed on completion, stonework was supported on arched cast-iron beams which were left in place.*

## PONTCYSYLLTE

*Previous page: The aqueduct viewed from Trevor Basin.*

*This innovative structure, opened in 1805, is discussed on page 27. With the vision required for such a break with convention, Telford's design took engineering to a new level. Indeed, in* The Iron Bridge, *Neil Cossons and Barrie Trinder describe it as 'a monument of the Romantic Movement as well as the Industrial Revolution.'*

*Above and facing page: To the south of Pontcysyllte is the Chirk aqueduct, its limelight stolen by its more famous neighbour. What appears to be a conventional viaduct is strong enough to carry the canal by virtue of using iron plates instead of puddled clay as its base. Flanged and bolted sides were added later to form a complete trough. The railway runs a parallel course over the river Ceiriog. Immediately to the north, the canal runs through a short tunnel which uniquely at the time included a towpath (left).*

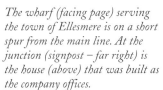

*The wharf (facing page) serving the town of Ellesmere is on a short spur from the main line. At the junction (signpost – far right) is the house (above) that was built as the company offices.*

*Beyond the offices stand the original workshops (right), now used by British Waterways, with two centuries of alterations in evidence. The original dry dock (above right) is today used by a commercial pleasure boat company.*

# 3  A RETURN TO SCOTLAND

**Roads, harbours and churches**

Telford first re-involved himself with the country of his birth in 1790, discussing possible improvement of the east-coast harbours with the government-sponsored British Fisheries Society. A half-century after the English army under Cumberland and Wade had ruthlessly destroyed the clan system, London had finally decided that Scotland needed social assistance.

In a small number of cases the harbour works extended to a wider brief. The Society had planned new towns at Ullapool and Tobermory before Telford's involvement, but he offered subsequent advice to both schemes. Uniquely at Wick he had a brief of his own, to plan a new settlement south of the harbour. Named Pultneytown, in addition to its well-planned residential spaces, it included what has been claimed as the first industrial estate, with workshops for all the trades associated with the fishing industry. In the nineteenth century Wick became a prosperous town, and fascinating remnants of it survive today.

The plan to help the fishing industry also included proposals for wide-ranging improvements to the roads, both in the Highlands and Lowlands which of course included bridges. Later, the Church of Scotland, having a government grant, requested help for a series of outlying churches and manses built to a standard plan (with a choice of one- or two-storey manse). Discovering these churches, scattered across the highlands and islands often in wild and dramatic locations, makes for a rewarding tour.

These schemes may not seem of much significance, but together they added up to a large body of work. While no one item would add to Telford's reputation (for the Caledonian canal, see Chapter 6), the whole programme reveals an admirable social commitment to his native country, particularly considering that he waived his fee to the Fisheries Society. Would a high-flying architect of today include in his workload forty low-budget village halls?

**Bridges**

Iron does not feature greatly in Telford's work north of the border. Apart from the swing-bridges on the Canal, the beautiful span at Craigellachie and a long lost one at Bonar, all his bridge work was in stone. While we can think of iron as being the new material he took and used to perfection, it is instructive to note the progress of masonry design. Even in his first Scottish bridge, Tongland, he used the technique of internal bracing walls rather than rubble infill for strength combined with lightness. Over the next two decades the visual appearance of his bridges changed from the early gloomy and gothic look to the careful detailing giving apparent lightness to Dean and Pathead.

All this work in Scotland fitted in with his many other commitments. Despite local supervision (and one of his strengths was picking able men for his team) at least once a year Telford undertook a highland tour to check progress in person. With thousands of miles to cover on horseback or pony-trap, it is no wonder he wanted to build the best possible roads.

*Facing page: Lovat Bridge, Beauly river*

*Above: A pre-Telford bridge on a track in Glen Lyon shows the need for improvement.*

*Tongland (above right and facing page), was Telford's first bridge in Scotland since Langholm. Although heavy-looking, it uses his technique of hollow masonry with internal bracing walls.*

*A comparison of Tongland's gothic pedestrian/flood arch with a detail of Pathead (right), built twenty years later (see page 47), shows how Telford refined the visual appearance of his bridges.*

*Right: A boy fishes for brown trout in the Waters of Leith, beneath Dean Bridge. The flatter arch of the pavement section gives an apparent lightness to the whole structure.*

*Ten miles south of the city at Pathead (facing page) the same detailing is employed. This viaduct shows the trouble Telford took to keep his roads level: to cross the Tynewater valley with a small bridge involves neither a detour nor steep gradients.*

*Facing page: Luikhart, in the Grampians.*

*Above and top left: Rannoch and Foss, on Tayside.*

*Right and above right: Plockton, north of Kyle of Lochalsh, with interior and manse (far right)*

Most of the lines of Telford's roads were so well chosen that they still exist today, albeit under layers of tarmac. However, on the A87 by Loch Cluanie, several original stretches are still visible, and where they are above the modern road, old stone-block retaining walls can still be seen.

*Right: The ruins of one of General Wade's military roads (built following the 1745 rebellion) leading into a Telford section, with the modern road beyond.*

*Facing page: 'The Mound' was built to provide a shorter route past Loch Fleet. The tollhouse (above) is at Conon Bridge.*

*Dunkeld, over the Tay (facing page), Ballater, over the Dee (left) and Ferness, over the Findhorn (above) are three of many associated with the road-building programme.*

## EAST-COAST HARBOURS

*Most of Telford's improvements to the east-coast harbours consisted of simple stone-built jetties to give mooring and shelter for small fishing boats. Cullen (right) is an unaltered example. Banff (below right) has had more quays added. Peterhead has been hugely altered, and the old lighthouse (far right) marked an original entrance.*

*Facing page: Aberdeen already had a large harbour, but the addition of the North Pier, seen here with a pilot bringing in an oil rig supply ship, provided shelter to the whole bay.*

*As further south, simple jetties predominate, unaltered at Fortrose (facing page) and Portmahomack (below right).*

*Invergordon is now a huge oil rig repair yard, but sections of Telford's stone-built quays are still visible. Captain Iain Dunderdale has 'Deputy Harbour Master' on his hard hat, but 'Cruise Development Manager' on his business card. Apparently tourists call in to marvel at the rigs en route to search for Loch Ness monsters.*

## CRAIGELLACHIE

For all Telford's skills as a mason, it was his use of iron that raises him to his pedestal. This bridge over the Spey, shining bright against its wooded hill, exemplifies the grace and lightness of structure that must have dazzled the world two centuries ago.

*Of the three sites on Islay, Risabus is a ruin (above), while Kilmeny (above right) and Portnahaven (facing page) are thriving parish churches.*

*Right: Members of the Board of Congregation inside Portnahaven's church. Telford's standard plan of two entrances is put to a unique use here, with one doorway used by the village and the other by the adjoining community of Port Wemyss.*

*North of Ballahulisch at Onich, the church has vanished but the manse (above) survives. Ardgour (below) is across the Corran ferry.*

*Duror (above and facing page) and its manse (right) are south of Loch Leven.*

*Berriedale church (below) sits high above the sea on the main road to Wick.*

*Croik church (right), ten miles inland from Bonar Bridge, is worth a diversion as it bears unique witness to the mass clearances of the early nineteenth century, when tenant farmers were evicted from the land in favour of sheep. Telford's unaltered church was built in 1823; in 1845 eighteen evicted families, huddled in the churchyard hoping for help, scratched messages on the east window of the church.*

Telford built a bridge and a harbour in Wick. More importantly, he planned the layout of a complete new town, Pultneytown, to the south of the existing settlement. The plan, which offered guidelines but not detailed archi-tecture, climaxed in Argyll Square, an elegant oval filled with sycamores (right).

Pultneytown brought prosperity to the far north. According to Tony Sinclair (facing page), a director of the Heritage Centre, the plan included the world's first industrial estate: built in close proximity to the workers' housing by the harbour (far right) were herring gutting and curing yards (centre right) and workshops for all the trades associated with the fishing industry. A ruin of a ropeworks still stands further up the hill (below right).

Pultneytown was incorporated into Wick in 1903. In 1940 some of the first German bombs fell by the harbour: is this the only British town still with unrepaired world war damage? In 1971 architectural advice to the council was to demolish most of the housing of Pultneytown. Fascinating fragments remain, scattered amongst streets of modern housing.

The roundhouse (behind Tony Sinclair) was built by Telford as a single-storey dwelling. It was bought by Mr Bremner (a 'wreck-raiser') who found it too small. As an engineering experiment he jacked up the whole stone-built house intact and added a new ground floor.

These two pretty west coast harbour-towns were built by the British Fisheries Society. They were already planned by the time Telford was involved in 1790, but he did offer advice to both schemes. At Tobermory he improved the quality of the stonework in the harbour (facing page) and ruled against further cutting away of the cliff, suggesting housing on the higher level (Breadalbane Street, top right).

Ullapool still has its church (right) but Telford's harbour work has been completely overtaken. Behind the front his advice to plan wide streets is very evident – new town style a hundred years ahead of its time. His suggestion to build a covered market directly behind the harbour was not taken up, but that is exactly where the stalls stand for today's Saturday traders (above left).

*Famous as a birthplace of
British christianity, Iona also has
its Telford church (facing page)
and manse intact.*

*Ulva (right) is tiny and
remote. Its church survives, but
with no congregation it is hard to
maintain. The Rt. Hon. Mrs J.M.
Howard, who owns the church and
the island, lives in the original
single-storey manse close by.*

*Mull has three unusual two-storey
manses, including Salen (below)
with added bay windows.
A heavily altered manse stands in
Tobermory, while the best is
reputed to be at Kinlochspelvie,
where there is also a recently
altered church.*

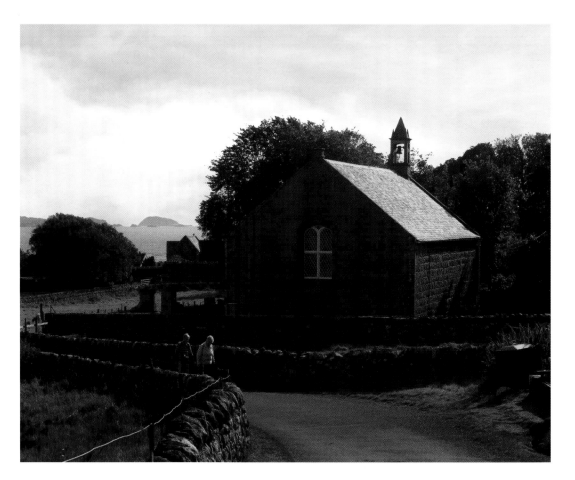

*What a pity there is no proper access to these two fine bridges, both of which stride across tree-choked ravines. At Hamilton (above right) an abandoned tollhouse (above) could easily provide the start of a route down to the river Avon.*

*A measure of the scale of Cartland Crags (left) is that it is known locally as a suicide spot.*

*Facing page: The gates of the Cartland Crags toll now stand at the entrance to the livestock market at Lanark. This is entirely appropriate, as cattle droving was a prime purpose for the road.*

# 4   THE HOLYHEAD ROAD

At the beginning of the nineteenth century, Britain's roads were, in general, in a worse state than when the Romans departed. Even the most important routes were the responsibility of individual parishes or separate turnpike trusts. There was little incentive for maintenance or improvement.

Despite its strategic importance as the route to Ireland, the main Holyhead road was no exception. Particularly to the west of Shrewsbury it was often no more than a cart track, and on Anglesey it was said to be a mere grassy path. A new government initiative overruled the accepted proposition that each trust would be responsible for its own little section, and in 1810 Telford was commissioned to report on the state of the whole route from London to Holyhead. In 1815 funds were voted for him to build a modern coach road of consistent standard throughout.

This enterprise produced some of his most inventive work. Even as the new road left London he stamped out one of his enduring principles: that a steep gradient cannot be tolerated on a modern road. Archway cutting bypasses the steep climb to Highgate (the iron bridge that gave the area its name came later). Telford even managed to keep to this policy as the route ran through Snowdonia: although a new turnpike road had been attempted two decades earlier, his skilfully graded Nant-ffrancon pass must have seemed at the time nothing short of a miracle (especially to the horses).

It was on the Welsh sections of the road that Telford's bridge-building again did him proud. Crossing the Menai Straits – a rough and sometimes impossible boat passage – posed a serious engineering challenge, but Telford came up with something radically new: a giant suspension bridge with a main span of nearly 600 feet, soaring 100 feet above the sea. As at Pontcysyllte two decades earlier, many thought the plan impossible. That he succeeded was no doubt due in some measure to his association with William Hazeldine, the iron founder who was by then producing wrought iron from his forge at Upton Magna. It was the properties of wrought iron that gave the suspension chains their strength.

Conwy has a similar bridge built in miniature and it is tempting to see it as a model for Menai, but in fact work on the larger bridge got underway first. At Bettws-y-coed the cast-iron bridge over the Conwy river was not so much a technical breakthrough as a visual one: cast into the outer ribs are the words 'Built in the year the Battle of Waterloo was fought.' North Wales is indeed a treasure trove for Telford's ironwork.

The toll house at Montford Bridge (see page 18) is one of the few features remaining on the English sections of the road (facing page). The milestone is a mile west on the A5 road.

Ty Isaf, into Wales past Llangollen, has the distinction of its weigh house as well as toll house remaining.

*At Waterloo Bridge Telford showed a rare moment of flamboyance: cast into the outer ribs of this iron bridge, built in Wales by a Scot for the English road to Ireland, are the emblems of leek, thistle, rose and shamrock. A shame so many travellers on the A5 speed across and never see them!*

1815

THIS ARCH WAS CONSTRUCTED IN THE SAME YEAR THE BATTLE OF WATERLOO WAS FOUGHT

*Past Lake Ogwen, the Nant-ffrancon pass, Telford's road clings to the hill above a huge retaining wall, keeping the gradient at a maximum of 1:22 (above). To the left of the wall can be seen the grassy remains of a turnpike road – an attempt to improve the route some two decades earlier.*

*Above right: Pont Pen-y-benglog crosses Afon Ogwen just below the summit of the pass. Telford's arch has been extended to widen the road, so bridging the remains of the older turnpike structure.*

*Stone-walled 'depots' (right), for storing road-stone for repairs, were built regularly throughout the final sections of the road (this example is on Anglesey).*

*Facing page: Into the mountains after Capel Curig the milestones become regular features (ms37 seen here has Tryfan in the background).*

*Previous page: Panoramic view of the Menai Bridge from Beech road, Anglesey.*

*The Menai Bridge was another wonder of the age (see page 75), although the original chains have been modified to cope with today's traffic. Seeing the bridge from a boat in rough weather (facing page) underlines what a hazardous stretch of water the Straits can be. Waiting for the sun can take a long time in North Wales, and Telford certainly was not deterred by a few raindrops.*

*The 'sunrise' gate (above), by the south side anchoring tower, is typical of those used at tolls along the road.*

*Right: The tollhouse at Llanfair*
PG *is arguably the best preserved*
*example on the Holyhead road,*
*and is complete with its original*
*tariff (above).*

*Facing page: The Stanley*
*Embankment, just before*
*Holyhead, took the road straight*
*through a coastal swamp which*
*previous routes had not even*
*attempted. The sluice allows tidal*
*flow, as well as white-water canoe*
*practice. Telford's line is now by-*
*passed by a parallel road, from*
*which this picture was taken.*

This delicate suspension bridge was not a model for Menai, but built after it. Castellated towers stand in sympathy with the castle beyond.

Here the 'sunrise' tollgate is matched by a pedestrian version (right). The detail (above) shows the iron bolts, part of the original suspension chains.

# 5 CANALS: TOWARDS THE AGE OF RAILWAYS

## Telford, troubleshooter

After Ellesmere, Telford's reputation made him the man in demand for canal companies with a problem. Projects with which he became involved included Beeston Lock on the Chester canal (the vital link between the Ellesmere's two sections), the three-mile-long Standedge Tunnel on the Huddersfield Narrow Canal (where work from the two ends was failing to meet in the middle!) and Harecastle Hill on the Trent and Mersey.

By 1815 Harecastle Hill tunnel had become a bottleneck. When Brindley built it half a century earlier it was considered an engineering masterpiece. But there was no towpath (boatman 'legged it' through - lying on their backs and pushing against the roof with their feet); worse, it was narrow and provided only one-way traffic with queues of boats incurring costly delays.

Rennie had been commissioned to drive a second tunnel, and when he died in 1822 Telford took over his scheme. This was to include a towpath, though the canal was still not wide enough for boats to pass, the plan being to run one-way traffic in conjunction with the existing tunnel. When it opened in 1827 it had taken less than two years to build, compared with Brindley's original, which had taken nine.

## New line to Liverpool

While the navvies were still at work under Harecastle Hill, Telford was asked to advise on improving the canal west of Birmingham. His proposals were nothing short of revolutionary.

Canals had grown up with the concept that they should follow the contour lines, winding their way circuitously to achieve their destination. Attempts to create more direct routes had been burdened by all the extra locks needed to go up and down the hills, entailing extra construction cost, a slowing down of traffic and additional need for water supply to the summit levels.

Utilising cuttings of previously undreamt-of dimensions, Telford determined that the new Birmingham canal would be both straight and level. If Brindley's canals could be likened to country lanes, Telford's new concept was a motorway.

By the late 1820s the railways were being seen by the canal companies as a potential threat to their traffic. In response to a proposal for a Birmingham and Liverpool railway, the Birmingham canal company asked Telford to survey a similar route for a new canal – enough apparently for the railway company to withdraw its plans. Telford's line for the Birmingham and Liverpool (today part of the Shropshire Union) embraced his brave new policy – straight, wide and level. There were new problems to surmount, caused largely by the intransigence of two landowners, forcing the canal on to lower ground to avoid a deer park and a pheasant wood. The huge embankments needed at Shelmore and Nantwich proved unstable and slippage caused literally years of frustration. The new canal eventually opened in 1837, two years after Telford's death.

*Beeston lock on the Chester canal (facing page) had been built on quicksand and constantly leaked. Telford solved the problem by lining the insides of the masonry with iron plates (a technique he had employed on the Chirk aqueduct).*

*Standedge Tunnel, over three miles long under the Pennines on the Huddersfield Narrow Canal, had a construction problem. Working from both ends, it was discovered that the two sections would fail to meet in the middle! Telford was drafted in and managed to minimise the inevitable 'S' bend at the meeting point. The photograph (right) shows the east portal at Marsden.*

*Facing page: At Telford's Harecastle Hill tunnel northern exit (with Brindley's original to its right), the redness of the water is due to seepage from iron workings inside the hill. The towpath is today out of use, as deep in the tunnel the whole canal has sunk — the suspended white-painted iron chains (below) indicate available roof clearance inside. One-way traffic is supervised by British Waterways 'helmsman' Mel Bryan, seen here inspecting the tunnel roof.*

# BIRMINGHAM, GALTON BRIDGE

*At the junction of the old and new levels west of Birmingham (right) the right branch connects through locks to the old system while Telford's new low line goes straight ahead, passing under Galton Bridge (facing page) as it enters the Smethwick cutting. Cast iron is by Horsley (below).*

*Rotton Park Reservoir (pump house and control gear, right and below) provides the water for old and new levels. The canal-sized supply passes industrial wharves, then crosses Telford's new line on the Engine Arm Aqueduct (facing page) before dropping through locks to the lower level.*

*Above: To the west of Wolverhampton, the new canal parts company with the existing Stafforshire and Worcestershire at Autherley Junction.*

*Original buildings include a warehouse (roof vent, far right) and lockkeeper's cottage (right).*

*The rubbing post (left) at the junction shows how cast iron can be worn away by hemp rope.*

AUTHERLEY. JUNCTION.

NANTWICH 39. MILES.

NORBURY

Facing page and above: Three miles north of Autherley, Belvide Reservoir provides the water supply at the top level of the canal.

Half a mile further it crosses the Holyhead road (the A5) in a cast-iron aqueduct dated 1832 (right). Telford built similar aqueducts at Nantwich and Macclesfield.

## BANKS AND CUTTINGS

Telford's 'straight and level' policy (see page 91) necessitated earthworks on an unprecedented scale.

Unstable ground meant Cowley tunnel (facing page) had to be shortened from its planned 600 yards to only 80. Tyrley rock cutting (below) shows how hard some of the digging must have been.

Right: the road 'tunnel' at Shelmore is a measure of how high the bank above is, with the canal out of view on the top. Both Shelmore and Grub Street remain unstable, costing British Waterways millions in maintenance.

Below right: A British Waterways tug pushes a barge of road-stone for towpath repair into the deep gloom of Grub Street cutting.

# 6 BIG CANALS AND ADDITIONAL EXCURSIONS

**Caledonian canal**

The exception to all the humble work Telford undertook in Scotland was the Caledonian canal. This project, spanning the years 1810 to 1822, is a singular major achievement, the fruit of vision and perseverance (despite the fact that by 1840 it was nearly closed down, not being deep enough for the increasing size of ships). The engineering difficulties can be exemplified by the building of the sea locks at each end, which at Corpach had to be cut out of solid rock, while at Clachnaharry the masonry had to be built up from beneath a deep bed of soft mud.

**Gota canal**

In 1808 a message from King Gustav of Sweden reached Telford on his travels, requesting his assistance with a ship canal linking the North Sea with the Baltic. This was a huge project. Despite the volatility of European politics, which might have ruled out any long-term co-operation, Telford spent many weeks surveying with the canal's instigator and propagandist, Count von Platen, with whom he remained a lifelong correspondent. Although he was able to offer much advice, put in place many improvements and delegate some of his own lieutenants and expert workers to help see the project through, prime credit remains with von Platen.

**Gloucester and Berkeley canal and the River Severn**

In 1817 Telford was appointed consulting engineer to a government body, the Exchequer Loan Commissioners, and could thus be said to have had some involvement in every major engineering project from then on. In the case of the Gloucester and Berkeley (known today as the Sharpness canal), built to by-pass the treacherous currents and sandbanks of the tidal Severn below Gloucester, he had a positive role both in management and in engineering.

Between 1823 and 1827 Telford was responsible for three important River Severn bridges, of cast iron at Holt Fleet and at Mythe, and an unusual one of stone at Over, the Severn's lowest crossing.

**Additional excursions**

At about the same time as Over bridge was being built, Telford assumed responsibility for the road to Milford Haven (for Ireland). By planning the route to Monmouth via Ross in order to avoid the Forest of Dean, Telford missed more than just steep terrain: his surveyors, writing to him in London, as well as noting 'a very objectionable hill at Longhope,' refer to 'intoxicated and Lawless Fellows from the Forest.'

Successive generations of engineers were involved in schemes to keep the East Anglian drains from silting up. Telford worked with John Rennie on improvements to the Nene and the Ouse, and then on his own account on the New North Level.

Telford's only major work in London was St Katherine Dock by Tower Bridge, constructed in 1824. In 1820 he was invited to become the first president of the Institution of Civil Engineers, and in 1821, for the first time in his life, he had a home of his own. At 64 years old, the man who was always on tour was finally thinking of settling down.

*Facing page: Fort Augustus on the Caledonian canal*

*Left: The canal's western terminus is at Corpach, near Fort William. Just to the east is the canal's most famous feature, the flight of locks at Banavie known as Neptune's Staircase – seen here with an* RNLI *boat ascending en route from Islay to Buckie. The white house (above) was Telford's residence during his visits.*

*At the north-eastern end Inverness has two marinas (above); within a mile the canal enters the Beauly Firth through a sea lock at Clachnaharry (facing page).*

The only original swing-bridge on the Caledonian canal is at Moy (above and facing page), just to the west of the summit cutting at Laggan. The aqueduct at Loy, one mile west (left and far left) with its heavy masonry tunnels for farm traffic and the river passage underlines the lightness of Moy's iron structure.

Facing page: The bridge at Moy is split, pivoting from each bank. Bridge-keeper Andrew Walker keeps the southern wing open, closing it as needed for farm traffic. When a large boat requires the whole canal width, he has to row over to open the north section.

## LAGGAN SUMMIT

*At Laggan the canal lifts up from Loch Lochy to its highest level; the white building (right) is the original lock-keepers house. To the north west is the Laggan Cutting (facing page), its depth disguised by a plantation of Scots Pines.*

*Beyond, the canal joins Loch Oich; this summit level, indeed the whole canal, is supplied by water from the River Garry (below). Norman Hill (below right) is the bridge keeper of Aberchalder swing-bridge, at the east end of Loch Oich.*

*Facing page: The cruise ship* Juno *enters Skorsvik lock. The cast-iron double-lift bridge (relieved by the adjacent modern one) bears a strong resemblance to the split swing-bridge on the Caledonian at Moy. Indeed, in his book* Swedish Cross Cut, *Eric de Maré claims it was imported from England.*

*Right: The canal's construction and mechanisms owe allegiance to a Scottish consultancy, but there is a distinctly Swedish look to the lockhouse architecture at Berg (date stone, 1820, below right) and to Elin and Ebba (below), summer season lock-keepers at Mem.*

*Right: Yachts climb the flight of locks from Lake Borens to Motala.*

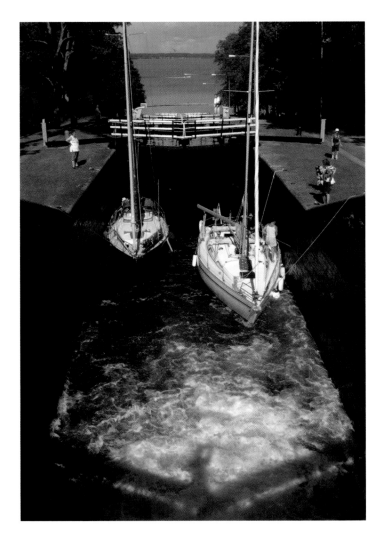

*In 1823 when Telford worked on the Gloucester and Berkeley (today the Sharpness canal), Gloucester Docks were already built. Telford increased the capacity with the 'Barge Arm' (right, with reflection of the National Waterways Museum).*

*Where the Gloucester and Berkeley crossed the Stroudwater, stop lock gates were used (left) to prevent one company 'poaching' water from another.*

*Facing page: At the old tidal basin entrance at Sharpness, the harbourmaster's house, a rebuild of the original, is now used by river rescue crews.*

*Facing page: The bridge at Mythe uses the same castings as Craigellachie. John Speck (right) hires pleasure boats at nearby Tewkesbury using the same wharf from which his grandfather worked as a bargeman.*

*Above: Holt Fleet, between Worcester and Stourport, has been substantially strengthened with concrete.*

*Above: Old Hill, Longhope, was 'very objectionable,' according to one of Telford's surveyors. On choosing a route to Monmouth, Telford avoided the steep Forest of Dean hills. At Huntley (tollhouse, left), his preferred line, the modern A40, can be seen taking a gentler grade up past May Hill towards Ross.*

*Facing page: The Severn Bore peters out at Over Bridge, the lowest crossing of the Severn. The unusual shape, copied from a bridge over the Seine, is said to better accommodate flooding, but not even the highest water comes up to the fluting; Telford may have had visual considerations in mind,*

*the design appearing to give the bridge a flatter arch (see page 44).*

*Telford considered Over a failure because it sank ten inches when the 'centering' was removed – but it has sunk not another inch since.*

*Left: At Cloughs Cross, the start of New North Level, the original brick structure contains modern sluices.*

*A footbridge (above) at Foul Anchor, where the Level meets the Nene, is unattributed to Telford, but has the look of his work with Hazeldine.*

*Facing page: The Nene Outfall, where the wide wet fens meet the North Sea.*

Late in life, Telford settled in a house in Great Smith Street, London, now demolished. The plaque (left) is today in the Institution of Civil Engineers.

Right: Telford asked to be buried at St Margaret's, his parish church in Westminster, but his colleagues argued for Westminster Abbey as the fitting resting place for such genius. His memorial is prominent in the nave.

Facing page: Apart from Somerset House, Telford's only work in London was St Katherine Dock, where his wharves and warehouses made imaginative use of a small space. Little remains of them today.

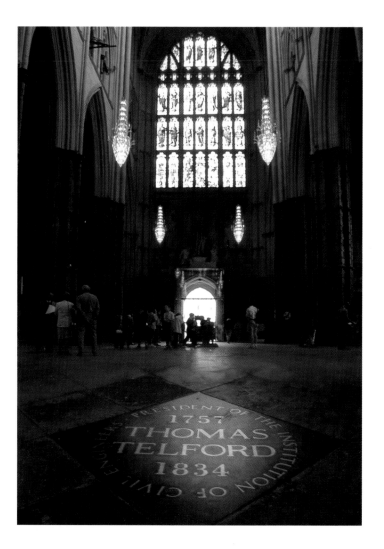

# TELFORD'S CANALS

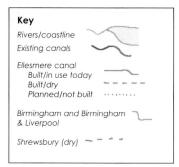

**Key**

*Rivers/coastline*

*Existing canals*

*Ellesmere canal*
  *Built/in use today*
  *Built/dry*
  *Planned/not built*

*Birmingham and Birmingham & Liverpool*

*Shrewsbury (dry)*

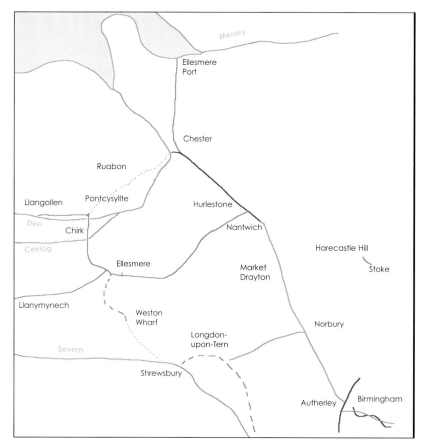

Mersey

Ellesmere Port

Chester

Ruabon

Llangollen

Pontcysyllte

Hurlestone

Dee

Chirk

Nantwich

Ceiriog

Harecastle Hill

Ellesmere

Market Drayton

Stoke

Llanymynech

Weston Wharf

Norbury

Severn

Longdon-upon-Tern

Shrewsbury

Autherley

Birmingham

# INDEX OF PLACENAMES

# BIBLIOGRAPHY

Bracegirdle, B. and Miles, P., *Thomas Telford*
Cossons, N. and Trinder, B., *The Iron Bridge*
Cragg, R., *Civil Engineering Heritage*
Dunlop, J., *British Fisheries Society 1786–1893*
Gibb, Sir Alexander, *The Story of Telford*
de Maré, E., *Swedish Cross Cut*
Quartermaine, Trinder, Turner, *Thomas Telford's Holyhead Road*
Quartermaine, *Telford*
Rickman, J. (ed.), *The Life of Thomas Telford*
Rolt, L.T.C, *Thomas Telford*

# ACKNOWLEDGEMENTS

Thanks for help and advice to:

Professor Angus Buchanan
Mike Chrimes
Neil Cossons
Jonathan Lloyd
Paul Manning
Jim McKeown
Rev. Henry Morris
Steve Morris
Lindsey Porter
John Powell
Michael Taylor
Barrie Trinder

Thanks also to all who agreed to appear in the book, and to:

AB Gota Kanalbolag
British Waterways
Church of Scotland
Institution of Civil Engineers
Severn Area Rescue Association
Shropshire Union Society
Ullapool Museum
Tobermory Museum
Wick Heritage Centre